POCKET

IQ

TESTS

TESTS TO STRENGTHEN YOUR MENTAL MUSCLE

E.J. PATRICK

FALL RIVER PRESS

New York

FALL RIVER PRESS

New York

An Imprint of Sterling Publishing
387 Park Avenue South
New York, NY 10016

Cover design by Modern Good
Interior design by Miles Parsons

ISBN 978-1-4351-2938-2

Manufactured in China

2 4 6 8 10 9 7 5 3 1

www.sterlingpublishing.com

TEST YOUR IQ

ABOUT IQ TESTS

LINGUISTIC INTELLIGENCE

LOGICAL-MATHEMATICAL INTELLIGENCE

INTRAPERSONAL INTELLIGENCE

NATURALISTIC INTELLIGENCE

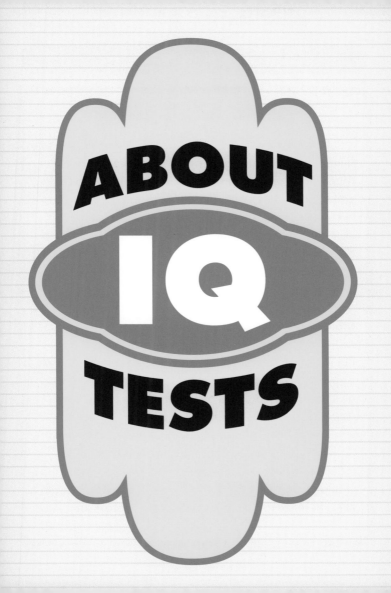

About Intelligence

Not even brain chemists, clinical psychologists, or human behaviorists agree on what intelligence is. Much of our everyday understanding is based on context: life factors relating to age, peer group, and even environment. To understand intelligence in context, as it is commonly measured and defined by IQ (Intelligence Quotient) testing, it helps to draw a parallel between the abstract concepts of intelligence and, say, maturity or morality.

For example, one can't identify the parts of the brain where specific quotients of maturity or morality reside, analyze them, and measure them scientifically. But it is easy to see that an adult individual who makes disparaging remarks about another in a loud voice at a dinner party could be called immature. In the same regard, few would question that an adult individual who steals from a child would be considered immoral.

But reduce the ages of the immature or immoral individuals from adult to three years old and you wouldn't judge them the same way. Context makes all the difference to our understanding in these examples.

Context impacts our understanding of intelligence in a similar way.

Intelligence, then, is observable and measurable through the behaviors and abilities of individuals as opposed to direct measuring and testing. A child who runs out into traffic is not considered less than intelligent. An adult who does so might be.

The IQ tests in this book can be used to measure certain types of responses that lead to conclusions about the intelligence level of the test taker. Those conclusions are what we commonly refer to as intelligence quotient, or IQ.

Overall, the conclusions drawn from IQ tests are based on different aspects of problem-solving ability. Speed is a critical factor in measuring problem-solving. For example, Thomas Edison is considered a genius. He holds the patents on more than 700 inventions. If a large number of engineers working for an industrial corporation over a period of 100 years invented 700 things, you wouldn't call them geniuses. The fact that Edison, one man, made so many breakthroughs so quickly makes him a genius. He had an exceptional ability to analyze a situation, review options, draw upon his own knowledge and experience, reach conclusions, and make choices that led him to brilliant solutions. Why brilliant? The whole world has access to the same information Edison had. But only Edison processed information in a way that led him to perfect the light bulb.

How You Can Use Intelligence Tests

You can use IQ tests not only to measure your own problem-solving capabilities, but to strengthen them and improve your scores. Think of an IQ test as something that tests the ability to learn and problem-solve, more than as a measurement of whether you are smart or not.

When used in an educational setting, IQ tests are only one component for determining a student's placement in a grade or curriculum. Many other behaviors factor into the ability to learn and the assessment of learning level. A low score on an IQ test, which on the surface is indicative of problem-solving ability, may also reflect ability to take a test or experience in taking tests, among other things.

So it is important to keep in mind that an IQ test is not so much a test as it is a confirmation. It is one way of confirming your progress as a problem-solver and should be used as a tool to help you advance your mental resources. For many people, a strong score on an IQ test, or a score that is improved over the last time, in itself is enough to boost the development of brainpower and mental agility.

Most experts agree that we are all born with a certain basic IQ that cannot be dramatically altered. Experts say that over the age of eighteen the adult IQ (which averages 100) remains fixed. However, to be accurately calibrated to any scientific degree, it must be calculated by clinical psychology professionals in comparison to a control group of tests performed on others of one's age. Further, one's performance on an IQ test can be improved by the repeated exercise of testing. Just like a muscle, the brain benefits from regular exercise.

The tests in this book are not comparable to the complex, scientific ones administered by a clinical psychology professional. They are not intended to be, nor do they have the same goal. This book is designed to help you have fun at home, alone or with friends and family, self-testing your intelligence-related responses in categories such as language, numbers, memory, and problem-solving skills. You can use the questions repeatedly to build your strength, and learn more about yourself!

Types of IQ Tests

This book includes four sections covering the most popular areas of IQ testing: linguistic, logical-mathematical, intrapersonal, and naturalistic intelligence. You can pick and choose which tests to take, or take them all. As a group, the tests in this book are designed to give you a well-rounded picture of your abilities that scores you both on the "feely" and "cold calculating" side. If you enjoy taking the tests and scoring yourself, seek out other tests that help provide more information in the areas you enjoyed the most, or that take you in yet another direction.

Tips for Taking IQ Tests

The best way to take an IQ test is the same as the best way to take any other test. Don't rush, but don't dally either. The ability to answer questions and problem-solve in a limited time period is part of the test. Everyone could get 100 if they had several weeks to answer the questions.

Have confidence in yourself, think through the question, and write your best answer. If you simply don't know the answer, search yourself to be sure, then give your best answer and move on. Remember, this is a learning experience and it is supposed to be fun.

Scoring Instructions

Give yourself a 50-minute time limit for the first two portions of the test, 25 minutes for the first section (Linguistic Intelligence), and 25 minutes for the second (Logical-Mathematical Intelligence).

Give yourself a 30-minute limit for the last two portions, 15 minutes each (Intrapersonal Intelligence and Naturalistic Intelligence). These two sections are subjective tests. Their results will reveal aspects of your personality and emotional profile. It's important to set a time limit on these so that you are sure to answer spontaneously, providing the basis for a true profile.

Scoring of the last two sections is included with the answers in the back of this book.

Scoring for the first two sections is as follows:

55 - 66	Exceptional
40 - 54	Excellent
30 - 39	Above Average
25 - 29	Good
15 - 24	Average

Scoring for the second two sections of the book is included with the answers starting on page 92.

LINGUISTIC

INTELLIGENCE

Sequencing Challenges

 1 **What comes next in this sequence?**

Apple, Pizza, Green Beans, Butter

a. Bread

b. Noodles

c. Lemonade

d. Banana

2 What word, when added to each letter or group of letters below, forms another word?

C

Ch

Thw

Sm

3 Rearrange the words below so they form new words.

WRONG

RAIL

STANCE

WORDS

Clarity Is King

Pick the right word for the following sentences.

4

Sam is talking to his _____ behind the garage.

confident   confidant

5

Someone forgot to set the alarm, so the _____ didn't go off.

censor   sensor

6

She has a degree in literature and spent many years as an English _____.

tudor   tutor

7

I would like you to explore this _____.

further   farther

What Works?

From the following lists of words, pick two that mean the same thing and one that means the opposite of those two words.

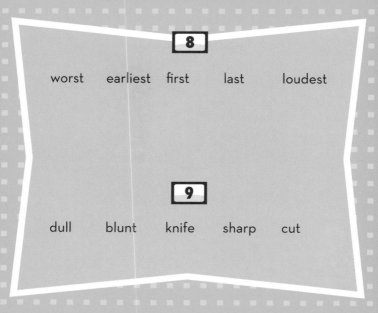

8

worst   earliest   first   last   loudest

9

dull   blunt   knife   sharp   cut

10

original   make   copy   paper   duplicate

11

talk   yell   shout   whisper   write

Anagram Madness

12

Rearrange the letters of each word to find the name of an animal.

HEROESAS

LAMCE

KITJABCRAB

13

Rearrange the letters of each word to find the name of an animal.

LIVENWORE

HOTRICS

MALLRADIO

Thought Connections

What one word ties each group of three words together? For example, the answer to the first question is "chair."

14

easy – high – lounge

15

flood – pilot – flash

16

tooth – ice – guitar

17

body – crossing – life

Word Play

Provide a synonymous rhyming pair of words for each of the things listed below. For example, the answer to the first, "Amorous crow," is "Flirty birdie."

18 Amorous crow

19 Alphabet garment

20 Village jester

21 How come tears

LINGUISTIC INTELLIGENCE

Word Whiz

What one word is being described by each two-word item listed below? For example, the answer to "Bake the novel" is "Cookbook."

26	Bake the novel

27	Ground-level feathers

28	Radiation tuber

29	Automobile song

30	Above the clock

LOGICAL-MATHEMATICAL

INTELLIGENCE

Series Challenge

In the series of numbers below, finish the series by filling in the blanks.

31 192   96   48   24   12

———   ———

32 9   22   10   22   11

———   ———

33 3   7   5   9   7

___   ___

34 3   4   12   4   5

20   5   ___   ___

The Shape of Intelligence

In the series of shapes below, circle the shape least like the others.

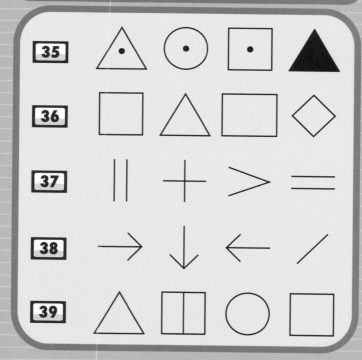

Smart Fives

40 Arrange five 5s so that they equal 6 without using any addition or subtraction signs.

Grandpa's Quiz

41

Grandpa Smith is 54 years older than his son, James. This year both the digits in his age are prime numbers and, when reversed, reveal his son's age this year.

How old are Grandpa Smith and his son?

Coding Quiz

The numbers 4513, 3154, and 1354 are codes for
three of the following words: RATS, STAR, and ARTS.
Work out the codes for each of the four words.

42

RATS

a. 4513

b. 3154

c. 1354

d. 4512

e. none of the above

43

STIR

a. 4513

b. 3154

c. 1354

d. 4512

e. none of the above

44

STAR

a. 4513

b. 3154

c. 1354

d. 4512

e. none of the above

45

ARTS

a. 4513

b. 3154

c. 1354

d. 4512

e. none of the above

The Test of Age

46

Tony is 6 years old.
Tammy is 10 years old. How many years ago was
Tammy twice as old as Tony?

a. 1
b. 2
c. 3
d. 4

47

In how many years will Tony be
three-fourths the age of Tammy?

a. 2
b. 4
c. 6
d. 8

48

How old will Tony be when Tammy is 20?

a. 10
b. 15
c. 16
d. 22

49

How old will Tammy be when Tony is 30?

a. 26
b. 28
c. 32
d. 34

School Smarts

50 Order the following European cities from north to south:

a. Frankfurt, Germany

b. Stockholm, Sweden

c. Madrid, Spain

d. Athens, Greece

51 Order the following U.S. Presidents from first in office to most recent:

a. Calvin Coolidge

b. Ronald W. Reagan

c. Jimmy Carter

d. James Madison

52 Order the following inventions from earliest to most recent:

a. typewriter

b. automobile

c. telephone

d. radiography

53 Order the following planets from largest diameter to smallest diameter:

a. Jupiter

b. Mercury

c. Venus

d. Mars

54

Order the following particles from smallest to largest:

a. quark

b. electron

c. molecule

d. proton

55

Order the following colors from longest wavelength to shortest wavelength:

a. yellow

b. violet

c. blue

d. red

56

Order the following roman numerals from highest to lowest:

a. XVIII

b. III

c. IV

d. LX

57

Order the following measurements from shortest to longest:

a. millimeter

b. yard

c. centimeter

d. kilometer

58

Order the following cooking measurements from smallest to largest:

a. teaspoon

b. ounce

c. tablespoon

d. gram

59

Order the following stringed instruments from smallest to largest:

a. sitar

b. viola

c. cello

d. violin

Go Figure

60

Sam has 20 coins in his pocket. Exactly one-fifth of them are quarters. There is only one dime. There are twice as many pennies as nickels. How much money does Sam have in his pocket?

61

Excluding 0 and 1, what is the smallest square number which is also a cube number?

62

What does X + 0 equal?

63

Sarah goes to the store to buy 28 bottles of soda water, priced at 7 for $3.84. Using only pennies, nickels, dimes, and quarters, what is the fewest number of coins Sarah needs to make her purchase?

64

Solve for y: 1/3+2y=1/3

65

Jake needs to buy some notebooks. A large notebook costs $5.00 and a small notebook costs $3.00. How much money will it cost to buy fifteen large notebooks and seven small ones?

66

Which is the better bargain? Jeans that are marked down 10 percent from the original price and then reduced an additional 40 percent or the same jeans reduced 50 percent from the original price?

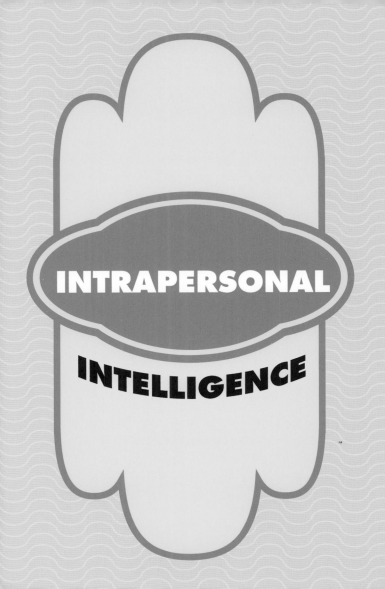

INTRAPERSONAL

INTELLIGENCE

Emotional Understanding

Don't think too long about these questions. For a true gauge of your intrapersonal intelligence, your answers should be spontaneous. If none of the answers exactly matches your response, choose the one that is closest. Be honest!

67

Your partner says something that makes you angry. You:

a. Walk out and slam the door. Stay at a friend's house that night to teach him or her a lesson.

b. Invest hours over the next few days coming up with a way to get back at your partner.

c. Work off your feelings in strenuous physical activity.

68

Your child wanders off at the shopping mall. After searching for an hour in panic, you finally locate him or her. You:

a. Spank the child soundly on the spot.

b. Explain, as patiently as possible, why it is important to stay near you.

c. Scream your head off and take away the child's privileges.

69

You observe a co-worker dishonestly managing a situation toward his or her own selfish ends. You:

a. Spread the word, then plot with your fellow workers to get back at this person.

b. Tattle to the boss.

c. Confront the dishonest co-worker yourself.

70

The last time you didn't get something that you badly wanted, you:

a. Tried to forget about it and moved on.

b. Cried until you felt better.

c. Obsessed for days about life's unfairness.

71

You are strongly attracted to someone who doesn't appear to reciprocate your feelings. You:

a. Invite the person to lunch and let him or her know how you feel.

b. Cry in your room and then try to put the person out of your mind.

c. Ask someone else to find out how the person feels about you.

72

Your next-door neighbor aggravates you beyond endurance by routinely cranking up his lawnmower at 7 A.M. every Saturday. You:

a. Buy ear plugs.

b. Mention it to him when you next meet on the street.

c. Get out of bed, lean out the window, and yell.

73

You learn that a public figure whom you admire has committed a craven, dishonest, or unseemly act. You:

a. Rant and rave about it to everyone you know.

b. Decide that people are garbage and you will never place your faith in anyone again.

c. Feel disappointment and sadness, initally, then accept that your hero, like everyone else, is flawed.

74

You are rejected or insulted by someone in your life who never seems to have anything good to say about anyone or anything. You:

a. Feel sorry for this person.

b. Bite your tongue and nurse a grudge.

c. Say something equally biting and critical in return.

Personal Understanding

75

You receive an expensive Christmas gift from a friend to whom you have sent something much smaller and less costly. You feel:

a. Like pond scum.

b. Grateful.

c. A little guilty but happy to learn the friend thinks so highly of you.

76

You and a friend are in a foreign country where you do not speak the language. You would like to ask a passerby to take a photo of the two of you, using your camera. You:

a. Pantomime your request, not caring if you're making a fool of yourself.

b. Wait until you can find someone who speaks English.

c. Forget about it because it is too much trouble.

You arrive at a party only to find that you are significantly under-dressed for the occasion. You:

a. Go home and change.

b. Have a good laugh at yourself.

c. Explain to everyone why you are not more dressed up.

78

Someone shouts a crude insult at you as you walk down the street. You:

a. Keep on walking as if you didn't hear the insult, but seethe inside.

b. Turn around and shout an equally crude remark back.

c. Laugh it off.

79

You have to get up in front of a small group of your peers to give a presentation. You are:

a. A nervous wreck, obsessing about your potential failure.

b. Nervous, but determined to do the best that you can.

c. Calm and self-confident.

80

Someone you know fairly well pronounces your name incorrectly while making introductions. You:

a. Let it slide.

b. Take the person aside later and gently correct him or her.

c. Do nothing but obsess about it.

81

Someone pays you a compliment. You:

a. Politely say "thank you."

b. Humbly deny your worthiness.

c. Smoothly wave it aside.

82

You consider birthdays, anniversaries, and holidays:

a. An obligatory pain in the neck.

b. A time to unload stress and party hardy.

c. Occasions that can be both trying and rewarding.

83

When you are introduced to new people you:

a. Usually remember the face but not the name.

b. Usually remember the first name.

c. Immediately forget most of what you've been told about them.

84

On most Monday mornings you:

a. Wake up with a feeling of dread in your stomach.

b. Have a hard time waking up.

c. Just get up and do what you have to do.

Personal Mastery

85

When you are sick, you are notoriously:

a. Miserable to be around.

b. Unstoppable no matter how bad you feel.

c. Not happy about it, but you do the best you can.

86

A friend tells you that your hairstyle is unflattering. You:

a. Take it to heart and get a new haircut.

b. Feel so wounded you never want to speak to your friend again.

c. Share an equal criticism of your friend's appearance.

87

A formerly fat friend shows up at a party having lost weight and shaped up. You feel:

a. Surprised and a little resentful.

b. Genuinely happy for your friend.

c. Self-loathing caused by your own physical condition.

88

A group of your closest friends have all been invited to the same party. You have not been invited. You:

a. Show up at the party anyway.

b. Have a party of your own, and make sure you do not invite the person who excluded you.

c. Write it off as a simple oversight.

89

You have been invited to the housewarming party of someone you barely know. You:

a. Don't go.

b. Send a note and a small gift.

c. Attend the party and take a nice gift.

90

When you are really down, your reaction is usually to:

a. Mope around, having no energy for anything.

b. Go on a shopping spree.

c. Eat or drink excessively.

91

Watching the TV news, when the story is particularly gripping or moving, you:

a. Comment aloud.

b. May cry.

c. Get annoyed at people in the room who are verbalizing or making other noise.

92

A clerk in a shop hovers too closely while you browse. You:

a. Calmly ask to be left alone while you shop.

b. Do nothing, even though you are annoyed.

c. Leave the shop.

Confidence IQ

93

You go to see a movie with friends. You dislike the movie intensely. However, your friends can't stop talking about how great it was. You:

a. Articulate your dislike of the movie.

b. Pretend you liked it.

c. Decide that maybe you judged hastily and should see it again.

94

You've spent the entire evening on the phone and finally have a moment to yourself before bed. Then a friend calls, desperate for a shoulder to cry on. You:

a. Gently explain why you can't talk right now.

b. Give up and, although resentful, listen.

c. Make up an excuse to get off the phone.

95

You have a serious personal problem to which there is apparently no ready solution. You:

a. Worry endlessly.

b. Lose yourself in an unrelated activity in hopes that an answer will pop up from your subconscious.

c. Call your best friend and ask his or her advice.

96

A man approaches you on the street with a long sad story and asks you to help him out by giving him money. You:

a. Reach into your wallet for a couple of dollars without giving it a second thought.

b. Look the other way and get away as fast as you can.

c. Suggest the man find the nearest shelter or travelers' aid facility, and give him directions, if possible.

97

You see a potential problem arising from your boss's current business strategy. You:

a. Keep your thoughts to yourself.

b. Consult with a fellow worker.

c. Discuss your concerns candidly with your boss.

98

If there is a window near where you are working, you:

a. Close the blinds because it is too distracting.

b. Open the blinds because you like to see what is going on outside.

c. Open the blinds, but don't get much work done.

Evolution IQ

99

In general, you find your partner to be:

a. Fairly demanding and high-maintenance.

b. Not demanding, but sometimes so passive as to be boring.

c. Always difficult, but you love him or her anyway.

100

In general, you would say that you are:

a. Patient and tolerant of your partner's quirks.

b. Fiery and passionate but extremely devoted.

c. Just as difficult as your partner, but loving all the same.

101

A member of the opposite sex flirts with your partner at a party, and your partner flirts back. You feel:

a. Jealous and angry.

b. Like laughing.

c. Sick and tired of it all.

102

Generally speaking, your goal for your children is for them to:

a. Have it better than you did.

b. Set their own standards and be all they can be.

c. Get out in the world and make their way like everyone else.

103 **Your priority for weekend and leisure time is to:**

a. Do something nice for yourself for a change.

b. Make sure everyone gets to their various activities as planned.

c. Just go with the flow.

104 **What would you do if you suddenly inherited a lot of money?**

a. Invest most of it, but give small gifts to family and friends.

b. Give most of it to charity.

c. Blow it on something really extravagant because life is short.

NATURALISTIC

INTELLIGENCE

Memory IQ

105

Do not turn the page either forward or back.

Do you remember, what was the background color of the previous page?

106

Give yourself ten seconds to study the list below. Then turn the page and make as complete a list as you can of the words.

Baby

Tuning fork

Tornado

Announcement

Horseshoe

Shamrock

Election

Roast beef

Birch tree

Family reunion

Potholder

Electron

107

From memory, list the words on the previous page below.

108

The menu at the diner featured a daily special of fried flounder, grilled potatoes, brussels sprouts, and macaroni and cheese, with a caesar side salad, lemon pie for dessert, and iced tea to drink.

Now turn the page and write down the daily special on the next page.

109

In the space below, write from memory the daily lunch special described on the previous page.

110

Give yourself ten seconds to study the following list of colors. Then turn the page and see if you can write the complete list of colors in order from memory.

Pink

Blue

Saffron

Black

Lime green

Goldenrod

Red

Forest green

Purple

Write, from memory, the complete list of colors in order as they appear on the previous page.

112

Give yourself ten seconds to study the list of animals on this page. Then turn the page and write the list from memory on the next page.

Monkey

Dog

Zebra

Snake

Swallow

Horse

Butterfly

Cat

Giraffe

113

What was your answer to question number 85?

114

You have a job interview at 11:00 A.M. tomorrow for the position of data processing manager at Crenshaw Brothers Warehouse, located at 1102 Vineyard Street, Suite 169, St. Louis, Missouri 63114, phone (314)246-7398. Your contact is Jerry Villanova at extension 233. Now turn the page and write all this down from memory.

115

Write from memory the complete information from the previous page.

Time of interview:

Position:

Name of Company:

Address:

Phone:

Contact name:

What Are You Thinking?

116

In casual conversation with friends, which one topic below best describes what you are most likely to talk about?

a. Politics
b. Food
c. People
d. Books

117

How much of your day is spent in worry? Choose one answer.

a. All of it.
b. Most of it.
c. Some of it.
d. None of it.

118

How often do you share your innermost thoughts with friends? Choose one answer.

a. Frequently
b. Sometimes
c. Rarely
d. Never

119

When you look in the mirror, what do you see? Choose one answer.

a. Someone I like.
b. Someone I can't stand.
c. Someone I am not sure about.
d. Someone who is okay I guess.

120

What is your prevailing view of the world? Choose the one answer that is the closest.

a. The world is a good place overall.
b. The world is evil and there is no hope.
c. The world is a mess but we can fix it.
d. The world isn't my problem.

1. d. Banana
2. Cart, Chart, Thwart, Smart
3. GROWN, LIRA/LAIR/ LIAR, ASCENT, SWORD
4. confidant
5. sensor
6. tutor
7. further
8. earliest first last
9. dull blunt sharp
10. copy duplicate original
11. yell shout whisper
12. SEAHORSE, CAMEL, JACKRABBIT
13. WOLVERINE, OSTRICH, ARMADILLO
14. chair
15. light
16. pick
17. vest
18. Flirty birdie
19. Letter sweater
20. Town clown
21. Why cry
22. Beach peach
23. Space race
24. Fat rat
25. Roach coach
26. Cookbook
27. Lowdown
28. Lightbulb
29. Cartoon
30. Overtime
31. 6, 3
32. 22, 12

33. 11, 9

34. 6, 30

35. ▲

36. ▭

37. ||

38. /

39. ⊟

40. 5.5 plus .5 plus 5 minus 5

41. 71 and 17

42. b. 3154

43. e. none of the above

44. a. 4513

45. c. 1354

46. b. 2

47. c. 6

48. c. 16

49. d. 34

50. BACD

51. DACB

52. ACBD

53. ACDB

54. ABDC

55. DACB

56. DACB

57. ACBD

58. DACB

59. DBCA

60. $1.45

61. 64

62. X

63. 63

64. x 0

65. $96.00

66. 50 percent

Scoring for the Intrapersonal Intelligence section:

Add up the number of "a, b, and c" answers you chose. If the total number of "a" answers varies no more than 2 points from the total numbers of "b" and "c" answers, you are a relatively mature, well-balanced individual. You have learned to fairly well control the needy child within yourself by developing adult ways to meet your own needs while respecting those of others.

If your "a" answers outnumber your "b" and "c" answers, you might want to take a look at some of your insecurities. We all have them, but you are acting them out a bit too demonstratively, and not always finding the best channels to express yourself. You are a sensitive person, and thoughtful, with a good sense of humor, and an excellent friend.

If your "b" answers outnumber your "a" and "c" answers, you have a calculating mind. This can be your best friend or your worst enemy. When you apply your mental powers to a situation you are a formidable opponent and can achieve any goal. But you sometimes hurt others with your designing ways. You don't do anything half way, so you are reliable and strong—but you may want to learn some moderation.

If your "c" answers outnumber your "a" and "b" answers, you are a passionate and emotional person—a true friend and loyal hard worker. You feel everything deeply and this is good, but you sometimes go over the top and find you have to reel yourself back in. Balance in life is the key to your happiness and you are always seeking it. Keep up the good work. Remember that to love others you must first love yourself.

Scoring for the Naturalistic Intelligence section:

Memory IQ:

If you correctly remembered 50 percent or more of the information asked for in this section, congratulations, you have an above-average memory.

If you remembered between 25 and 50 percent, you have an average memory.

If you remembered less than 25 percent, you could use some further memory-stimulation exercises. Keep working at it—you have room to improve.

What Are You Thinking?

Your personality is revealed by your answers as follows.

116. a. You are an analytical thinker.
  b. You are ruled in large degree by your senses.
  c. You are curious, sensitive, and concerned about what people think.
  d. You are hungry for information, something of an escapist.

117. a. You aren't yourself lately and should seek a healthy way to vent your concerns.
b. Think about rejuggling the pressures in your life so you have more balance.
c. You are normal and healthy.
d. You are either a highly evolved individual or perhaps not a fan of reality.

118. a. You are lucky to have good friends—but are you giving them enough time to talk?
b. You are well-balanced and on an even keel emotionally.
c. You are probably a little too tightly wound.
d. You should find someone to talk to.

119. a. You are a healthy, happy individual.
b. You should seek to find the source of your issues with yourself. Talk to a friend, or maybe a counselor.
c. Have a little more faith in yourself and remember that none of us feels totally confident all the time.
d. You are like most people, doing fine day by day.

120. a. You can't go wrong with this positive attitude.
b. You are a self-fulfilling prophecy.
c. You are someone who will leave a constructive mark on the world.
d. You are pretty immature.